Miss Mac
The Church Cat

by Miss Mac
ably assisted by Fr John Chaloner

A Redemptorist Publication

Published by **Redemptorist Publications**

Copyright © 2004 Redemptorist Publications

Text and Illustrations: John Chaloner
Layout: Rosemarie Pink

First published in 2004
Third Printing September 2005 (6th thousand)

ISBN 0 85231 293 8

Printed by
Coltec Parker Limited, Keighley, BD21 3LG

Alphonsus House Chawton Hampshire GU34 3HQ
Telephone 01420 88222   Fax 01420 88805
rp@ShineOnline.net   www.ShineOnline.net

CONTENTS

CHAPTER ONE

As it was in the Beginning

I t has to be said that not many cats write books. This, you will understand, is not through lack of talent but through lack of opportunity. I am fortunate enough to have the services of a scribe. I shall begin by telling you who I am. I have been given the name Macavity, known as Mac. There is nothing very original about the name, of course. We all know that T.S. Eliot thought of it long ago when he wrote about Macavity the Mystery Cat in *Old Possum's Book of Practical Cats*. Well, it's true. Every cat *is* a mystery. I think I was given the name because no one knew where I came from.

I was found, you see, by two children one August day. They were playing in their grandparents' garden alongside the road that takes you from the little village of Dunsop Bridge into the Trough of Bowland. They heard me miaowing because I was stuck in a fence. I was only a kitten and how I got there I just do not know. But they rescued me, called their grandmother and I was taken into the house.

I wasn't there for long as their two dogs objected strenuously and I was put into a big cage inside a large wooden building at the back of the house and given some food and milk.

Now there is one thing you must understand right at the beginning. Cats can understand everything people say. Some people can understand a little of what we say, but we cats can understand *everything*. Some of what you are about to read comes from what I have heard people say, often when they thought I was asleep. And so it was that I heard the family talking.

"Does anyone know where this kitten has come from?"

"No. I've telephoned people locally and nobody has lost a kitten."

"It must have been dumped here then. That's what people do. They drive into the Trough and dump their animals. There's lots of stray cats around here."

"The children would like to keep it, but what about the dogs?"

"No, we can't keep it. Have you tried the priest? He has cats, I think."

"Well, yes. He has had cats, four of them. Three were run over and one was shot, so he says he's reluctant to have another cat."

"Well, there's nothing else for it. We shall have to send her to the RSPCA."

The priest, I discovered, was their neighbour. He lived further down the road at the little church, but I'll tell you more about that later. The morning after he had been told about me, and while I was still in the cage, he had found himself wandering around a supermarket in the town looking for cat food. Why he was doing so, he did not really know, as he had convinced himself that he was certainly not going to have another cat and go through the pain of loss yet again. But some mysterious force, he said, seemed to drive him towards the pet shelf of the supermarket. That same force made him walk up the road that afternoon and knock at the door of the big country house.

"Have you still got the kitten?" I heard this voice say.

"Yes, but I'm just about to phone the RSPCA."

"Well please don't," the voice said. "May I see the kitten?"

The mysterious force that propelled him into the supermarket and along the road now almost immediately took him and me into his house. Within minutes I was accomplishing the remarkable feat of eating, drinking and, at the same time, miaowing, just grateful that at last I had somewhere to call my own.

The house was enormous, with lots of rooms, comfortable beds and chairs that I would soon claim as my own, and places in which to hide and sleep (but generally not to occupy more than once in any given day). All in all it was most satisfactory. The garden, as I was to discover, was even more satisfactory. Along the bottom ran a beck. It swept down from the hills and meandered beneath overhanging trees. At the back of the house was a small wood and in front of this were bird tables and nut cages. On these and flying around them were all kinds of birds – tits, finches, siskins, nuthatches, woodpeckers, jays, collared doves, jackdaws, pigeons and blackbirds. In the wood could be seen pheasants, a couple of mallards, rabbits and squirrels. People buy food for themselves and their cats from supermarkets, but here was a supermarket where everything was free. It took but a moment to decide that here I had come to stay. Sleep, born of food, warmth and contentment, soon overtook me, but not before I had gone through the process of ablutions required of all cats after a good meal and at other times during the day.

This blissful state of affairs continued for several days, interrupted only by brief visits to the garden to attend to the necessities of life.

The only ripple on the surface of this otherwise halcyon time was the priest's irritating habit of referring to me as "he". I was not "he" but "she". The truth was discovered about two months later when he took me to the vet. She told him that I was then about four months old and very definitely a "she". T.S. Eliot's Macavity was of course a male. Having given me the name of a male cat the priest was left in a quandary until he alighted on what *he* thought was a rather ingenious solution. From then on I was called *Miss* Macavity or Miss Mac.

My first excursion into the wood at the back of the house reduced the priest to a state of near panic. I heard him shouting all over the place, "Mac, Mac, where are you?" but I didn't bother. I was far too busy watching things. Besides, I felt I had to establish my independence at the outset of this relationship. Being stroked, cuddled, and played with is all very agreeable at the right time and place, but not when I have things to do. After a while, about an hour or so, I decided to make an appearance with the result that I was immediately swept into his arms and carried into the house.

"Mac, I thought I had lost you. Didn't you hear me calling you?"

I resolved that this sort of thing simply would not do.

* * * * * *

If that excursion brought him to a state of near panic, my first excursion into the wood across the road from the church succeeded in doing the job properly. I had tried to get across the road a couple of times before, but he had snatched me up just as I was about to make a dash for it.

"Don't go across the road, Mac. I've lost three cats because of that road and I don't want the same to happen to you."

Well, really, I thought, this is too much. This is bordering on paranoid behaviour. It did not take me long to elude him and get across the road. Once there, I crept deep into the wood and spent hours busily occupied. My return to the house brought the expected response.

"Oh, Mac, where have you been? I haven't seen you for nearly eight hours."

This man has got to learn, I thought.

* * * * * *

A couple of weeks later I climbed a very tall pine tree in the wood at the back of the house. It was still light when I made the ascent and,

"Mac! What are you doing up *there?*"

having almost reached the top, some fifty feet or more from the ground, I settled down in a spot where the branches formed a comfortable nest and decided that here I would spend the rest of the night. Then came the dark and into the wood came the priest, on what had by now become his routine nightly search.

"Mac, Mac, where are you?" and "Come on Mac, it's time to come in. I've got some nice food for you. Come on Mac."

But I was far too comfortable. An hour later, back he came, then off he went down the road, then all around the garden. Midnight came and the lights in the house were turned off. "Ah, peace at last," I said to myself. But it was not to be. The priest couldn't sleep and, dressing gown over pyjamas, back he came again. This time, a nearby branch snapped and this made him shine his torch up into the tree.

"Mac! What are you doing up there? Are you all right?"

Amazement at the fact that I was so high up in the world turned into panic yet again as he wondered what he should do. Immediate thoughts of calling the fire brigade were dismissed. He did not think they would take too kindly to his call. And so every hour during the night he came out to make sure I was still there. Finally, when dawn came I decided that I would come down. I had already taught myself to come down trees backwards and so it was easy enough to descend. Why he had been so worried was beyond me but I thought it was only right that I should let him know I was safely down. I went up to his room, jumped on the bed, put my face into his and purred. This of course woke him up.

"Oh, Mac! You've got down by yourself! What a very clever Macavity you are! I was so worried about you. I thought I would have to call out the fire brigade today."

Really, I thought, he does go on so.

* * * * * *

I think he now understands that I am quite capable of looking after myself. Or rather, I think he almost understands. Even now he still searches for me and if you were to go along the road at midnight, or even later, you might well come across him, torch in hand, wandering up and down the road, into the wood, around the garden of the church, into the wood at the back, calling for me. He likes to get me back into the house at night, but he doesn't always succeed, especially in the summer nights. But he has to learn to live with the fact that we cats are free spirits and have minds of our own. I think he has learned to live with it but you never can tell with humans.

"The priest is looking for you, you know."

CHAPTER TWO

The Angel and the Horse

"This 'ere church was built by an 'orse, you know," said Stanley.

"Don't be silly," I said. "How could a horse build a church?"

"It's right, I'm telling you. I've heard folk talk about it. Th'orse is buried in the cemetery 'ere."

I decided not to argue with him. You never get anywhere by arguing with Stanley. He is the ginger and white local tomcat and, like all tomcats, he has a rather inflated opinion of himself.

I had heard the priest talking to people who were visiting the church and *I* knew the real story. The little church had been built not *by* a horse but *with the help of a horse*. Kettledrum was a racehorse and there is a beautiful painting of him, surrounded by butterflies, high up in the apse of the church where there are paintings of other animals – a dog, a bull, and a deer. There are also four small carvings of a horse's head on the side pillars of the altar beneath the apse. Kettledrum, owned by Colonel Charles Towneley, was very special. In 1861 he won the Derby, beating the favourite, Dundee, by a length. At odds of 16/1 he brought in a prize of 11,550 sovereigns and the story is that some of the money was used to build the church. It was Colonel Towneley who had the church built, not Kettledrum. Stanley had got his facts wrong.

"You see that statue of an angel over there," said Stanley. "Well, that's where th'orse is buried."

Wrong again, I thought. I did not know where the horse was buried, but it was certainly not in the cemetery and certainly not underneath the angel's statue. It was best to say nothing. Stanley would not have listened and anyway he wasn't the only one who thought Kettledrum was buried in the cemetery. I have heard visitors to the church ask the priest, "Now tell us, Father. Where's this famous horse buried? Is it near that big angel?"

The statue of the angel is indeed large and also very beautiful. It stands guard over the burial vault of the Towneley family. I could have told Stanley about the vault as I had been down to inspect part of it. That was when it was opened for the burial of Lady Mary Towneley. During her burial the hunting horns were sounded and I was there for that too. Her body had been brought into the church the previous evening. I had joined the family, stayed with them and the priest as they said prayers, then I had smelt the flowers on the coffin, and finally decided to spend the night in church with her. But I wasn't going to tell Stanley any of that. He would have pooh-poohed what I said, as he has this tomcat trait of treating lady cats as if they know nothing and do nothing. Even worse, he has never set foot inside the church, whereas I know the church intimately and spend many an hour in there as I shall tell you.

* * * * * *

What is more, at that time he hadn't spoken to the angel as I had. I was mooching around the cemetery one night when I heard this voice.

"The priest is looking for you, you know. He's gone into the wood over the way."

"Who are you?" I asked.

"I'm Goldilocks Aster, the Angel of Saint Hubert's."

"That's an odd name," said I. "I thought it belonged to a wild flower."

"Well, I didn't choose it," retorted the angel. "Given the choice I would not even have touched it with the tip of my wings. It's the name the priest has thought up for me. He's always giving names that bear no resemblance to reality. I don't know why he does it. I find it quite embarrassing."

"I know exactly what you mean," I said. "He names animals from books or theatrical productions. My name is a case in point and there were other cats before me. His first cats were called Grosvenor and Bunthorne from Gilbert and Sullivan's opera *Patience*. Then from *The Yeomen of the Guard* there was Cholmondeley."

"I know those operas well," she said. "I've heard the music played at some of the church concerts."

"He also had a cat whom he named Portia. That name…"

"Was from *The Merchant of Venice*," she interrupted. "I'm well acquainted with Shakespeare's works. Well, it is all rather irksome, but I suppose it keeps him amused. It reminds me of the names some people give their children in baptism. Once you're given the name, that's it. You're saddled with it for the rest of your life and sometimes the only thing you can do is to abbreviate it. But I'm certainly not going to abbreviate my name to Goldy or something equally fatuous. On the whole I choose to ignore it."

"I have always understood that angels were heavenly spirits and that they give messages to people," I said, mainly in an effort to divert her from going on about her name.

"Well, I'm giving you a message, aren't I?" snapped the angel. "I'm telling you that the priest is out looking for you."

"Not that sort of message," I said. "I mean messages with some spiritual meaning."

"Oh, we can't spend all our time on that kind of thing. You have to temper the spiritual with a bit of the material from time to time, you know. Anyway, I'm not that kind of angel."

"What do you mean?"

"I'm a static angel. The others are flying angels, but you seldom, if ever, see them. We static angels come in all sorts of makes and sizes. I'm made of marble. Some are made of stone, or plaster, or wood. Some are in oil paintings or water colours. Others," and here she took a deep breath, and sighed, "others are in *plastic*. But we all give messages, even if we don't all fly around delivering them. People look at me and get the message that there is more to life than can be found in this world alone, at least some of them do. There are heavenly things. As Saint Paul says, 'things which no eye has seen and no ear has heard, things beyond the mind of man, all that God has prepared for those who love him'. But, forgive me, perhaps that's going a bit too deep for you."

"Patronising angel," I said to myself. She obviously doesn't realise that I know a lot about heavenly things. What with Stanley, and with Goldilocks here, I've got a lot to put up with.

CHAPTER THREE

Saint Hubert and the Stag

T hat night, after the priest had finally caught up with me, I made a special point of going into the church. There are lots of heavenly things in here which the angel has never seen, I thought. Just like Stanley, she's never even crossed the threshold of the church.

First of all I looked at the glorious stained glass windows. The central west window is of the patron saint of the church, Saint Hubert. Now here is where there is a picture of yet another animal, this time a stag and he is seen standing with Saint Hubert. But he is a stag with a difference as between his antlers is a cross. One year, on Good Friday, I saw two deer. They told me that they had come down from the hills above the Brennand Valley and I once saw a deer run through the little wood at the back of the church and down to the Langden Beck. Another year, on Saint Hubert's Day itself, I met a stag in the wood opposite the church. But I had never seen a stag with a cross between his antlers. After all, I am a cat and cats miss nothing. So why, I asked myself, has this stag got this cross?

And so I jumped up onto the ledge below Saint Hubert's window and asked Saint Hubert himself.

"Hello," I said. "I'm Macavity, the Church Cat."

"Yes," he said. "I know. I've seen you in here quite often. You seem to be quite a devout cat, but may I point out a slight fault?"

"Certainly."

"Well, I've noticed that when people go to Holy Communion, they have to walk around you as you never budge an inch when you are in front of the altar."

"Oh. I'm sorry. I never thought about that."

"The other thing I've noticed is that you have a tendency to jump on the altar when the priest is saying Mass."

"Oh dear. I'm sorry about that too. It's just that I'm interested in what's going on."

"I see. Well, never mind. I'm sure you mean well. In what way can I be of assistance to you?"

"Well. It's about this stag and the cross. I've never seen a stag like that before, and I was wondering why he has got this cross."

"Why don't you ask the stag himself? He's here, beside me."

"Hello," said the stag.

"Hello. What's your name?" I asked.

"I'm called Soter," he said.

"That's another strange name. Why are you called Soter?"

"Well, obviously, it's Soter as in Soteriology, a word that has something to do with Salvation, I believe."

"That's an awfully pompous name," interjected Saint Hubert. "I have never called you by that name."

"No, that's true, you haven't," said the stag, somewhat abashed. "It's that priest. He's given me the name."

"Oh yes," said Saint Hubert. "I know all about him. Mind you, I suppose he's got a point. The Cross is a sign of salvation and it was when I saw it between your antlers that I was converted."

"You see," continued Saint Hubert, addressing himself to me, "hundreds of years ago, I was a nobleman and I spent an inordinate amount of my time out hunting. One Good Friday, when I should have been at church, I was hunting deer and I came across this stag – er, Soter here – and was just about to kill him when I saw this cross in between his antlers and on the cross the figure of a man. Now you will understand that this is not the sort of thing that is calculated to help your aim, and I must say that I was quite put off by it. And so, I let – er, Soter here – go, and off he ran. But it gave me a lot to think about, I might tell you. I came to realise that God must have been telling me something by giving me this vision, and so off I went and consulted Saint Lambert. He helped me to understand what God wanted of me and in due course I became a priest and then, in fact, I succeeded Saint Lambert as Bishop of Maastricht in 705."

"Is it because you saw this vision of the Cross that you became a saint?" I asked, not knowing quite what to say after all this.

"I don't like to think so. I hope it was because of more than that. Perhaps it was because I tried to love and serve God with all my heart. But you will understand that modesty prevents me from saying any more."

"Yes, of course," I said. "But tell me. Why is the church named after you?"

"Well, you see, I am the patron saint of hunters and this church is in the Forest of Bowland, which was once a royal hunting forest."

* * * * * *

This set me thinking. That he was the patron saint of hunters explained why I had come here and made it my home. Like all cats, but some more than others, I too am a hunter as it is in my nature to hunt.

And so I asked Saint Hubert, "Will you be *my* patron saint?"

"Perhaps," he replied. "But only if I find that you qualify as a hunter. Tell me about yourself."

"Do you want a sort of CV?" I enquired.

"Not exactly," he said. "A brief résumé of your hunting exploits will suffice."

"Will you be my patron saint?"

"I go out hunting every day without fail," I told him. "Usually I catch something. Will that do?"

"Oh, I think I need a bit more than that," he replied. "Does anything unusual ever happen?"

"Well, yes, it does. You see, more often than not when I take my prey into the house through the cat flap I find that the priest tries to catch it. Sometimes he is successful, but, of course, that is only if the prey is still alive."

"But of course," said Saint Hubert. "Do go on."

"You will understand that at first I was quite pleased with his response, as I take the prey not only to show him what I have caught but also to give him lessons on how to hunt as left alone he never seems to bother."

"Quite so," said Saint Hubert. "He doesn't strike me as being a hunter, although perhaps he does try to hunt for a few souls now and then."

"You can imagine my disappointment," I continued, "when I find that his efforts to catch the prey are aimed at *releasing* it. I have known him to creep on all fours – but in a poor imitation of what I can do – and reach underneath tables, chairs, and bookcases. He has run out of the front door followed by me, and then run out of the back door while I was still at the front, clutching a mouse or a rabbit. He has run into the wood in the middle of the night, when in his pyjamas, with *my* prey, and put it into a rabbit hole or into the bushes. At first this sort of thing really got up my whiskers. If whatever I have caught and brought into the house has already departed this life he doesn't seem to mind as much, but there can still be an awful to-do when he takes it out of the house and I try to bring it back in again."

"One has to learn to live with these odd goings-on in the human race," said Saint Hubert, consolingly. "But, tell me, do you ever lose your prey without this annoying intervention by the priest?"

"Yes, I have to admit that I do," I replied, downcast. "I am ashamed to say that there have been a few times, when the priest has taken his wellies from their stand in the hall, a small rabbit has popped out and scurried off."

"Any other times?" asked Saint Hubert, as if hearing my confession.

"Er, yes," I said. "There has been a time or two when, late at night, he has heard noises underneath the bookcase in his sitting room and found a rabbit hiding there. One night, in the space of two hours, he found rabbits in both locations, one underneath the bookcase and another in one of his wellies. All of these I had brought in earlier in the day, usually many hours earlier, and they had eluded even me."

"How fortunate for the rabbits," said Saint Hubert. "And where, may I ask, were you when these rabbits were found?"

"I was either out or in church asleep. I heard the priest talking about what happened. Excuse me for asking again, but do I qualify as a hunter and will you be my patron saint?"

Saint Hubert thought for a while, his eyes closed. He was obviously pondering on all that I had told him. Losing the rabbits will probably go against me, I thought. But then he opened his eyes.

"Losing one's prey happens even with the best of hunters," he said. "Look at me. I lost Soter here, and I'm very glad I did. Yes, I'm pleased to say that you qualify and that I will be your patron saint."

"Thank you, Saint Hubert," I said, "and thank you and Soter for your time."

"Don't mention it," said Saint Hubert. "Goodnight."

* * * * * *

I walked up to the other end of the church and settled down behind the altar. Fancy thanking them for their time, I thought. I should have realised that as they are in eternity they have no such thing as time. Never mind, they knew what I meant. Happy that Saint Hubert was now my patron saint, I slept the sleep of a contented hunter.

" ... I slept the sleep of a contented
hunter."

CHAPTER FOUR

Memories

"Look at this 'ere. 'E's left them gates open. 'E's always forgetting to close 'em. It's ridiculous."

It was Stanley again. He was sitting near the large wrought iron gates at the entrance to the church garden.

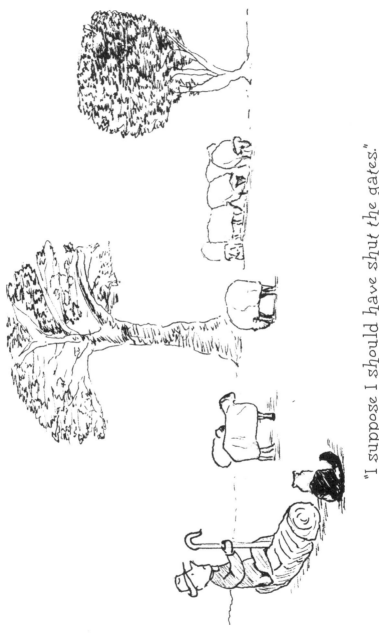

"I suppose I should have shut the gates."

"I've heard him say that he leaves them open so as to present what he calls an 'open house' to anyone who wants to see him," I said.

"Aye, 'appen that's all well and good in a town, but this is countryside, and things don't work quite the same way," said Stanley. "Sheep wander up and down this road and if gates are open they come in. I've watched it 'appen. I saw about twelve of 'em come in one day. 'E were chasing 'em all over garden."

"Did he get them out?" I asked.

"Well, of course 'e did or they'd still be 'ere, wouldn't they? 'E got them out through gates at bottom of garden. But it were ridiculous. 'E were running up and down after 'em but that made it worse. If you ask me, 'e's got no idea at all. I bethought myself, that'll teach 'im – but it didn't. 'E left 'em open again next week, and about same number of cattle came in."

"And did he get them out as well?"

"Well, 'e didn't. It were farmer as got 'em out. Drove all round garden on 'is quad bike, farmer did. Made a right mess an' all. 'E said to farmer, 'I suppose I should have shut the gates.' Farmer replied, ''Appen that's what gates are for.' But it's made no difference, if you ask me. 'E still leaves 'em open."

* * * * * *

"If you want to know about animals messing up the garden, I can tell you a thing or two," said a voice from high above the cemetery. It was Goldilocks, putting in her pennyworth.

"Years ago, there was a priest here who had a pig and a goat. Now if anything could make a mess they could. What is more they had a habit of wandering out onto the road and the priest would cajole unsuspecting walkers into driving them back. They weren't too happy about it."

"Who weren't? The walkers?" enquired Stanley.

"No, the pig and goat. But what was worse," Goldilocks continued, "he kept hens, and he kept them in the enclosure around the Towneley family vault, of all places, directly below me. They were scratching around, clicking, clucking, and crowing. The noise was something appalling."

"If you're talking about noise, what about the peacocks and peahens?"

The contributor of this remark was a passing pheasant. The red around his eyes reminded me of someone who had spent the night with a whisky bottle.

"What's your name?" I asked.

"Philonous the Pheasant. The priest gave me the ..."

"Don't tell me," I interrupted. "I know just what you're going to say. It's another very odd name."

"Well, really," said Philonous. "How rude. My name is found in all the best books on philosophy. But if you think my name is odd, listen to this. There was Percy Peacock and Penny Peahen and they had three chicks. The first was named by the priest as Petavius Peacock ..."

"After Dionysius Petavius, of course, a Jesuit historian and theologian of the seventeenth century." This intervention was from Stanley, and was given with a rather superior air. But then, his owner is very well read.

"If I may continue?" said Philonous. "The other two were called Ha'Penny and Half Pence." So as to prevent another elucidation from Stanley, he added quickly, "They were named after old and new money."

"How very clever," yawned Stanley.

"These were all the progeny of Percy," continued Philonous, "as was Sweet Pea, the daughter of one Prudence Peahen who had arrived here one bright morning and departed into who knows where about a year later. Their combined noise between March and August each year was quite out of this world."

"That's not quite true," said Goldilocks. "I'm from out of this world and I've never heard anything like it. Percy made the most noise. He used to sit on one of these grave stones near to me and shriek at people, cars, bicycles – anything that happened to pass by. I don't mind admitting that his noise almost turned me into a nervous wreck."

"I heard that Percy and Penny came from Dolphinholme, and that the priest offered them a home here when their owner emigrated," said Philonous.

"I'm not in the least surprised that their owner emigrated," replied Goldilocks. "That shrill, piercing call was enough to make anyone

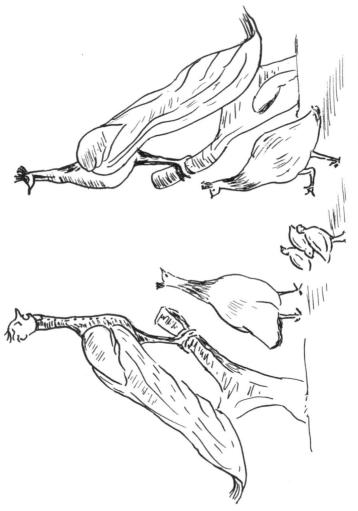

"Their combined noise ... was quite out of this world."

emigrate. I myself would have emigrated had I not been inseparably joined to this marble plinth."

"Percy took charge as soon as he got here," continued Philonous. "Prancing about, displaying his plumage and tail, telling all the animals and birds what to do, he was pomposity personified."

Stanley seized his opportunity. "Th' ancient Romans described peacock as a bird wi' feathers of an angel, step of an assassin, and the voice of a devil." He yawned again, stretched out his front paws, sat down and began washing himself. He is so smug, I thought. How I wish his owner were not so well read.

"How dare you equate his feathers with mine!" snorted Goldilocks. "My wings are quite heavenly. In any case, his feathers always fell out at the end of each summer. Mine never fall out."

"But one has to admit that his feathers were a sight to behold, especially when he displayed them," said Philonous.

"Perhaps," replied Goldilocks, grudgingly. "But his feathers were a mess when he first came here. He couldn't do a thing with them." She warmed to her story and went on, "He arrived inside a small trailer and he had lost a hefty bunch of feathers in transit. Of course, from where I'm standing I could hear and see all that went on. It was three days before the peahen came here. She'd gone missing about three weeks before Percy arrived and then she turned up at a farm a good few miles away. I could hear the priest muttering to himself, 'How am I going to collect a peahen in the car? It will flap around all over the place.' Then I heard someone tell him that he should get a cage. So he borrowed one from a local gamekeeper. A few days after he had collected her she went off again, as did Percy.

He came back but she was away for over a week until she was found at a farm in Newton, some three miles away as the crow flies."

"Or 'appen as the peahen flies?" suggested Stanley.

Ignoring him, Goldilocks continued, "Eventually she settled down. In fact, they all settled down far too well, if you ask me. They were here about four years."

"Where are they now?" I asked.

"They all went to a new home in a forest about ten miles away," said Philonous.

"Thank God," I said.

Goldilocks resumed her story. "They didn't all go at once. Petavius escaped and became the new peacock-king for a couple of weeks. When he was caught a local farmer came and somehow managed to put him in a sack so as to carry him

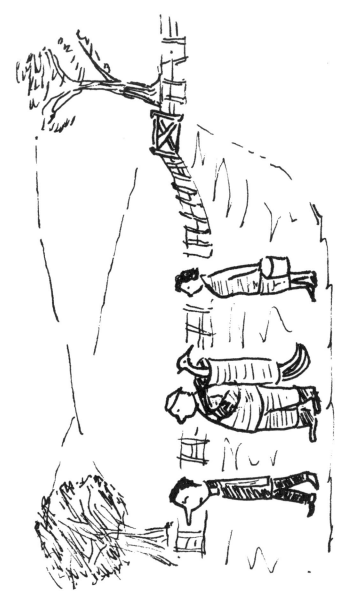

" ... like the beginning of some strange religious rite."

to the forest. I heard the farmer say that it was the best way to transport him."

"That would not have qualified as my preferred mode of transport," observed Philonous.

"Please do stop interrupting and let me finish my story," said an irate Goldilocks. "I saw them all go off. First of all, there was the priest in his clerical attire. Next came the farmer. He was carrying Petavius in the sack. Then came the farmer's wife. She was carrying a bucket of bird grain. I saw them drive off to the forest. I remember it was a May evening so they probably came across a rambler or two."

An enigmatic smile crossed her lips.

"I wonder what people thought?" she mused. "It probably looked like the beginning of some strange religious rite."

"Maybe the ramblers thought they'd drunk too much," suggested Philonous, brightly.

I bet you know all about that kind of thing, I said to myself.

CHAPTER FIVE

Lent and Easter
at Saint Hubert's

I n January and February there is always a
profusion of snowdrops in the church
grounds. The priest says that from medieval
times these little flowers were grown around
churches and monasteries and are known as Our

55

Lady's special flowers, sometimes called Mary's tapers, Candlemas Bells, or Maids of February. By March the snowdrops have given way to clusters of daffodils with glorious displays of yellow and white. Sometimes these clusters form circles in which, unobserved, I can either watch what's going on or bed down and fall asleep. We cats know that sleep is a necessary part of life and so we make of necessity a virtue, sleeping sometimes for hours on end.

* * * * * *

It had been a beautiful day, full of sunshine. I had spent much of the morning and part of the afternoon asleep in the daffodils. That evening when I came in from the garden I saw the lights on in the church and so I decided to investigate. The church was full of people. Along the north and south sides of the church there are paintings and at each of these the priest paused for a while. Then all the people joined him in saying some prayers. And so I followed him and every time he stopped before a painting I sat down. It did not take long before I decided that I'd had enough and so I jumped onto the altar and had a wash.

*   *   *   *   *   *

Later that evening I decided to have a word with Saint Hubert and ask him what it all meant.

"Hello, Saint Hubert. It's me again."

"Who is *me?* To whom am I addressing myself?" said he.

"It's Mac. You know, the Church Cat."

"Ah yes. How could I forget? Forgive me, I was dozing. Can I be of some assistance to you?"

"Well, yes, I hope so. Can you tell me what the priest and people were doing this evening?"

"Why certainly. They were making the Stations

of the Cross. The paintings are scenes from the journey Jesus made when he carried the Cross to Calvary to die for us. They help us to pray. This is the time of Lent. Soon it will be Easter and then we shall celebrate his Resurrection. You really must make a point of being around then."

"Thank you. I will."

He is so helpful, is Saint Hubert. I learn so much more from him than I do from Stanley or from that drunken pheasant. But Goldilocks is quite helpful at times, I must admit.

And so I did as Saint Hubert had suggested. One night I went into church and heard the people say this prayer:

> "Save us, Lord, while we are awake;
> Protect us while we sleep;
> That we may keep watch with Christ
> And rest with him in peace."

I said to myself, "Here is a prayer that I can call my own."

You see, a cat is an expert in the art of watching and resting. I often go into the church and sleep on the rug behind the altar. Indeed, the priest admits that I spend more time in church than he does. In the summer, sun or rain, I go under a rhododendron bush or a conifer tree and there I spend a large portion of the day either watching or sleeping. And I know exactly where to find shade and where to keep dry.

I went back into church the next day. The altar was bare, the statues were covered in purple cloth, no flowers were to be seen, no lighted candles.

"Why does the church look so sad?" I asked Saint Hubert.

"Today is Good Friday," he replied. "It is called 'Good' because on this day Jesus died for us.

But tomorrow evening we shall begin to celebrate his Resurrection. If you're not otherwise engaged, why don't you stop by the church tomorrow after dark and see what's going on?"

The following evening I watched as all the people assembled outside the church. A fire made from logs and twigs was busily burning and crackling. The outline of Stapleoak Fell could be seen in the dusk and I heard an owl in the wood. The priest lit a large candle from the fire and said, "May the light of Christ, rising in glory, dispel the darkness of our hearts and minds." Then the people, all carrying lighted candles, followed him into the church and he proclaimed three times, "Lumen Christi" – "Christ our Light." Beautiful flowers of every kind adorned the church and under the wrought iron altar a little garden had been made. Stones had been placed in the form of an empty tomb. A pebble path led to the tomb and in the corner of the garden were three crosses. All around, against a pale blue background, were flowers and plants. Nearby was a stone jar full of water.

I tried to settle down in the garden under the altar but it was rather uncomfortable. I contented myself with smelling the flowers and sitting at the side of the church. I was fascinated by all that was going on, particularly when the people carried their lighted candles to the front of the church and blessed themselves with water that had been poured into the font. So that night after everyone had gone I jumped onto the font and drank some of this water.

"Excuse me," said a voice from the back of the church. "Just what do you think you are doing?" It was Soter the Stag. "Not even *I* would dare to drink from that water."

"Why not?" I asked.

"The water was *there* and so I drank it."

"Because", he said, "that water is to be used only for baptism."

"I'm most awfully sorry," I said. "The water was there and so I drank it."

"You sound rather like Adam when he gave his excuse for eating the forbidden fruit," said Saint Hubert. "Look at all the problems *he* caused. I suspect the same could apply to drinking water simply because it is there. No, this really will not do."

I began to wish that I had never even seen the water.

"I never imagined for one moment I would upset you so much," I said. "I just like to join in with whatever is happening. I promise not to do it again."

"There, there," said Saint Hubert, soothingly. "Don't take it to heart. I'm sure we can find a substitute for the baptismal water. Now, let me think. Yes. I've got it. Look over here."

He pointed to the door of the church. "By the door is a holy water stoup," he said. "I think it will do admirably. You will find holy water stoups at the entrance to many churches. Some have been there since Norman times. People bless themselves with the water as they enter or leave the church. It can remind them of their baptism. That particular stoup was found near to the site of an ancient church that stood at Burholme, just a couple of miles away. I don't see why you can't have a drink from that, from time to time."

You see what I mean when I say that Saint Hubert is so helpful? No one else, not even the priest, would have thought of the holy water stoup as providing a source of refreshment. I found that by climbing onto the back pew I could stand with my front paws resting on the top of the stoup and my hind legs on the top of the pew.

Then, by gently lowering my head I could drink the water. It really was an excellent idea.

"Thank you so much, Saint Hubert," I said.

"Just a minute. What about me?" The intervention came from a very disgruntled Soter.

"All these years that I have been in this stained glass window with you, and never once have you suggested that I could drink from the holy water stoup. If any animal is allowed to drink from the stoup then that animal should be me."

"May I ask why?" enquired Saint Hubert.

"Because there is specific reference in the Holy Scriptures to my family's association with water. I can quote you chapter and verse. It is Psalm 41, verse 1:

'O God, my whole soul longs for thee,
As a deer for running water.'

There is no reference in Scripture, at least none that I can recall, to a small domestic cat."

"Small domestic cat indeed," I replied. "Far better to be a small domestic cat than a stained glass stag."

"Oh come, come," said Saint Hubert, addressing himself to Soter. "May I suggest that you are being just a wee bit peevish? I know that Miss Macavity here is a relative newcomer, but surely by now you must have realised that in the Church the first are often last, and the last are often first? It's all because of grace, you see. All that we are and all the good that we do are God's gifts to us. And so such things as family connections with Scripture or the length of time spent in a stained glass window count for very little I'm afraid. I know it's rather tiresome, but that's the way it is, and there's absolutely nothing you can do about it."

"Who is Grace?" I wondered. "Is this another name the priest has thought up?"

CHAPTER SIX

Walking in Water

I had been here only a couple of months when the priest took me down to the beck that runs alongside the bottom of the garden.

"Do you want to come for a walk, Mac? Come on then. Come on, Mac. Let's go for a walk."

And so I did. Walking with him by the beck has now become a regular feature of my life. Sometimes I drink from the water after first stepping carefully on the stones at the side. At other times he walks back to the house while I stay and hunt or sleep in the long grass.

There is always a lot of activity on the beck. At times a heron flies from a rock in mid-stream or oystercatchers circle above, warning us off. A procession of mallards and their young waddle along the bank and then process into the beck to bob up and down in the water as it carries them over the rocks. Or we might see a dipper singing as it stands on a rock before it disappears under water to emerge upstream and continue its song.

But our walks do not end at the beck. On the other side and across from the church garden is Mellor Knoll, a steep hill. Near the bottom is an area called the "Warren" and in the early summer this becomes a beautiful carpet of bluebells. How do I know? Because more than once I've been there with the priest. I've also walked with him along the cattle track by the "Warren", down on to a field, over a stile, and across the beck opposite the house where I was found.

I hear you ask, "How does a cat get across a beck?" and the answer is that the priest carries me. Rather he did carry me, quite a number of times, until one evening, while holding me in his arms, he slipped and we both crashed down into the water. He was smoking his pipe and this hit the bed of the beck first and smashed in two, possibly saving his nose from doing the same. He landed headfirst and stayed in a horizontal position for some time. I scrambled out, reached the other side and went straight up a tree. You can well imagine the scene that followed. A priest, soaked to the skin, standing at the foot of a tree and calling to an equally soaked cat near the top of the tree, "Mac, are you all right? Please come down. I'm awfully sorry."

Silly man, I thought, that's the last time I let him carry me across. I'll do it by myself next time. And I did.

I left it for a year or two, during which time the priest, embarrassed by what had happened, did not dare to take me across. One afternoon when the water was low I decided to show him what I could do unaided. I stepped onto the stones at the side of the beck. This was near to where we had fallen in before. Then, carefully focusing and weighing up all the implications – as only we cats can when making major decisions – I jumped about five feet across the water, landed on a rock in the middle, and then jumped again onto the rocks on the other side. He sat there, dumbfounded. That will show him, I said to myself. Of course, as was to be expected, he waded across the water after me, only this time he kept his balance. We walked back along the bank to a point past a gate into the church garden. This time he crossed first and I followed him, jumping a sizeable distance from one rock to another in mid-stream. I was determined not to let him carry me as by now I had learned that he was totally inept when it came to walking in water.

Long before the time when we both fell in the water I was walking with him along the beck and he spotted a lamb on the far side crying to its mother on the other side. And so what did he do? He waded across in an attempt to retrieve the lamb and carry it over to its mother. But of course when he got to the other side the lamb ran off. He gave chase but then gave up when he realised he was getting nowhere. And so he crossed back but slipped and fell in, while the lamb and its mother ran in parallel lines to a place upstream where the beck narrows. The mother sheep crossed and rejoined her lamb with the greatest of ease. I watched the priest, crushed by defeat and soaked to the skin, squelch his way home.

* * * * * *

One August day I was talking to Stanley about these goings-on. His territory includes the village of Dunsop Bridge and so he is very well acquainted with all that happens there.

"Oh aye," he said. "It's like this 'ere Duck Race that's held for your church at Dunsop every August Bank Holiday. 'Appen it'll be held again this year. That priest of yours gets wet every time."

"Why, what happens?" I asked.

"Well, it's like this 'ere. Folk all around buy tickets, each ticket is numbered, and each number goes with the number on each duck. Then all these ducks, about a thousand of 'em, are put into a big sack, and this 'ere sack is taken upstream to a bend in the river near Holme Head – and the ducks are emptied out into river."

"Excuse me," I said, "but isn't that just a little bit cruel?"

"Don't be ridiculous!" retorted Stanley. "I'm not talking about *real* ducks. I'm talking about *plastic* ducks."

"Plastic as in plastic angels?" I enquired.

"Eh?" said Stanley.

"Oh, never mind," I said. Best to leave it, I thought. He wouldn't understand. Anyway, that conversation with Goldilocks was private.

"When these ducks are emptied into the water," he continued, "folk wade along the river behind

"It's called 'Attention-Seeking Behaviour' so I've 'eard."

'em. They push the ducks along and shove 'em out from underneath the bank or from in between rocks. I've watched 'em do it."

"Why does the priest always gets wet?" I asked, my curiosity aroused.

"Well, because 'e's always there in the water wi'em, isn't 'e? No show without Punch, is there? The difference is," and here a sort of Cheshire Cat grin appeared (although he isn't a Cheshire Cat), "the difference is that 'e always slips on the river bed and goes right under. Other folk keep fairly dry, but not 'im. 'E usually falls in about three or four times."

"So what happens then?"

"Well, the first ducks under the bridge at Dunsop are the winners. Folk get prizes, if their numbers are the same as on winning ducks."

"And where do these prizes come from?"

"Folk as buy tickets give prizes. Sometimes they get back same prize as they've given."

"How curious" I said. "And then what happens?"

"It's like this 'ere. T'other ducks, them as aren't winners, 'ave to get back to finishing line, and then they're all gathered up and put back in this 'ere sack. Them as are wading follow on, including priest of course. But 'e always manages to slip under water again. I've sat on bridge and watched. When 'e goes under water, all the folk on village green and them as are in Puddleducks Post Office and Tea Room, they all let out a big 'Hurrah', and priest usually takes a bow. It's called 'Attention-Seeking Behaviour' so I've 'eard."

Sadly, for once I had to agree with him.

CHAPTER SEVEN

Cat in a Bonnet and Birds of a Feather

"This 'ere is Cordelia Cat," said Stanley. "Cordelia's come t' live in Dunsop. Cordelia, this 'ere is Mac."

"Very pleased to meet you," I said. "May I ask where you come from?"

"Well it's quite a long story but I'm here because of that priest of yours," she replied. "You see, I was staying at a farm a few miles away. There were lots of other cats there and whenever the priest visited the farmer and his wife he brought the cats some food."

"How interesting," I said. "I didn't know he fed other cats besides me."

"Oh yes, not only the cats on the farm but the dogs as well. In fact, I was told that he took them food which you had left uneaten in your bowl. I believe you are quite adept at hunting for your own sources of nourishment."

"That's true enough," I replied, and then added with not a small measure of pride, "Indeed, Saint Hubert himself has agreed to be my patron saint, you know. But I'm happy to share my food with others less fortunate."

"There's nowt in doin' that," interrupted Stanley. "God wants you t'share food you need, not what you've sniffed at and left in bowl, 'appen."

"And what's more," said Cordelia rather snootily, "until that priest of yours came along I was far from being unfortunate. In fact, I was very comfortably off on the farm. I would still be there if he hadn't whisked me away."

"Whatever do you mean?" I asked.

"Well, it all happened like this. The priest visited on a day when it was very cold and after he'd given us some food he went into the house to see the farmer and his wife. I went underneath his car to investigate – as one does – and decided to jump up underneath the bonnet. It was nice and warm near the engine and I must have fallen asleep because the next thing I knew I was being driven along the track and onto the road. It was, to say the least, a fur-raising experience, as you can well imagine. I clung on for dear life until all at once the car came to a halt. I heard a woman's voice calling out,

"'Do you know that there is a cat's tail hanging underneath your bonnet?'

"'Oh no!' cried the priest.

"Next thing the priest, obviously in a state of panic, opened the bonnet. I was certainly not going to hang around and so I flew out in a great flurry of fur and ran straight underneath a bush. The priest followed me and went down on all fours.

"'Kitty, kitty, come out! *Please do come out!'*

"I decided to stay where I was."

"Aye, 'appen I'd 'ave done t'same," said Stanley.

"All at once I seized an opportunity to escape from the bush and scamper into a barn and that's where I've stayed. I'm quite happy where I am. I have most of the creature comforts. But, as I say, it's your priest's fault that I'm here."

"I think you are being rather harsh on my priest," I said. "After all, he wasn't to know that you were underneath the car bonnet, was he? Anyway, what did he do after you ran away?"

"Well, when I was hiding in the bush I heard him say, 'How am I going to tell the farmer and his wife that I've lost their cat?' He was in a terrible state. I watched from the barn as he drove off back to the farm. Some time later I was talking to Fly the sheepdog. She had been helping with gathering sheep that day and she was in the farmyard when he arrived back at the house. She said the conversation went something like this:

"'Hello, Father. Didn't expect thee back so soon. What's up?'

"'I'm sorry to say that it is the tabby cat. A lady on a horse stopped me a couple of miles down the road and told me that a cat's tail was hanging from underneath the bonnet. The cat must have got inside the bonnet when I was with you. It was all right, I think. Well, it must have been. It ran off when I opened the bonnet.'

"'Ee, thar didne' need to bother tharself, 'appen. It's not our cat.'"

* * * * * *

"I reckon 'e's bit 'accident prone' as they say," observed Stanley, and then, addressing me, added, "Do you remember when 'e broke 'is 'eel? 'E were mowing lawn at time."

"How can anyone break a heel when mowing a lawn?" asked Cordelia, incredulously.

"It's true, I tell you," said Stanley. "I watched it 'appen. Lawn at back of 'ouse goes down t'driveway. There's about a five-foot drop on t'drive. Well, he mows up t' th'edge of lawn, y'see. Now I could 'ave told 'im what were goin' t'appen. 'E turns round wi' mower, but 'e doesn't turn round, if you get my meaning. 'E loses 'is balance on th'edge an' falls down on t'drive instead. Went wi' a mighty wallop, 'e did. And then mower comes down an' all and ends up on 'is foot. From then on 'e were like Jacob after 'e wrestled wi' th'angel, limpin' all over place."

"He was on crutches for months," I explained. "The good thing was that he couldn't pick me up at night to bring me in. Of course, he tried, but he could only go short distances on his crutches. Whenever he found me I took great satisfaction in walking off, knowing that he couldn't follow me."

"That seems very callous of you," remarked Cordelia.

This cat is beginning to irritate me, I thought. But then she did have a point. I remembered that I was also rather accident prone when I was a kitten.

"Yes," I admitted, "perhaps I should have been a little more sympathetic, especially as when I was younger there were a few times when he took me to the vet because I had injured myself."

"I were at vet's once," said Stanley.

"I've never ever been to the vet," said Cordelia. "We farm cats can look after ourselves."

By now she was annoying me intensely.

Stanley, who had noticed my tail swishing, diverted the conversation. "When I were at vet's your priest came in wi' that there peahen what had broken 'er wing, the one we were talking about before, remember? 'E were carrying 'er in a big cage 'e were and 'e looked fair worn out 'e did. I 'eard him tellin' vet that milkman 'ad put cage wi' peahen in it on 'is milk lorry in middle of crates of milk, like, an' brought 'er all way from Dunsop over fell while 'e'd followed behind in 'is car, 'appen."

"How extraordinary," I said.

"Aye, it were. Mind you," he continued, "it doesn't surprise me, doesn't surprise me at all. It's kind of thing 'e does. I mean, look at them there birds. 'Ave you ever seen birds as well fed as them? No, you 'aven't, neither 'ave I. It's 'cos 'e's forever feedin' 'em wi' bird seed."

At that moment a collared dove swept down onto the bird table and scooped up some food.

"See what I mean?" said Stanley. "It's ridiculous. Them birds know as they're onto a good thing wi 'im, 'appen."

* * * * * *

I was thinking this over when I strolled into church the following day and sat at the front of the altar as the priest was celebrating Mass. Drowsiness overtook me when he began to preach. Then all at once I sat up. The words that caught my ears were "dove" and "Holy Spirit". What on earth is he going on about? I wondered. That night I asked my friend, Saint Hubert.

"It's all quite simple," he replied. "The dove represents the Holy Spirit who came down to us after Jesus ascended into heaven."

"Like the doves in the garden sweep down on the bird food?" I asked.

"Er, well, not quite like that," said Saint Hubert. "You see, the Holy Spirit comes to fill our hearts with his love and is with us always."

Those doves will be with us always if the priest keeps on feeding them, I said to myself as I retired for the night on the rug at the back of the altar.

CHAPTER EIGHT

The Flight of the Hawk

I t was a bright and crisp December
morning. I knew that in the evening the
little church was going to be full to the
brim when people came from all around to join
in the Carols on Advent Sunday.

"Come on, Mac," said the priest. "We'll go for a walk. There will be too much to do this afternoon so we'd best go now."

As we walked along the side of the beck we both spotted a bird that neither of us had seen before. Perched high on a branch was a hawk. It was, as we later found out, none other than a Harris' Hawk. Standing underneath the tree were two young men who were trying to coax it down. But the hawk remained on the branch, aloof and impervious to their entreaties.

For many an hour that day I watched as the hawk moved from one tree to another, flew back over the beck and into the garden, flew from the garden and into the wood, whilst the men followed dutifully behind. At last it came to rest on one particular tree and there it remained.

I heard the priest call out to the men, "Would you like a cup of tea?"

"Nice one," they replied.

"Anything else I can do to help?" he called.

"Well, yes," one of them said. "The jess on the hawk's leg is stuck fast in between two branches and it can't move. Have you got a ladder?"

"Yes. I'll bring it."

"Nice one," they replied.

Of all the trees the bird could have chosen on which to be stuck fast it had alighted on one of the tallest Caledonian Pines and was perched at a point to which none of the ladders could reach and nobody could climb.

"There's nothing else for it," said one of the men, despondently.

"We'll have to call out the fire brigade."

"I'll phone them," offered the priest, helpfully.

"Nice one," said they.

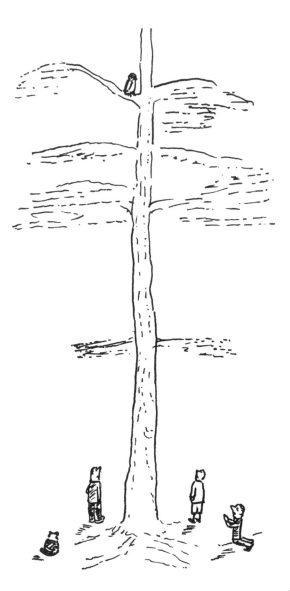

"… *the* hawk *remained on* the branch,
aloof *and* impervious *to* their entreaties."

By this time I had come into the house and I listened as the priest made his telephone call.

"Hello. Is that the fire brigade? You may think this request rather odd. It's not a fire that I'm reporting. It's a hawk stuck in a tree."

"That's no problem," said the kind lady at the other end. "We've dealt with stranger things. We're on our way."

"They are on their way," the priest called out to the men.

"Nice one," they replied.

About half an hour later I was asleep on the chair when one of the men came to the back door of the house.

"The hawk's got free. It's flown back across the beck. Sorry about this, but could you cancel the fire brigade?"

"Nice one," I heard the priest mutter under his breath.

For the rest of that afternoon neither hawk nor pursuers were to be seen. Evening came, dusk descended, but still no sign. Then just as people were beginning to arrive for the Carol Service there was a knock on the front door. I growled, as I often do when there is a knock on the door, and went to investigate. The priest opened the door and standing there were two dishevelled young men and one equally dishevelled hawk perched on and firmly fastened to the arm of its owner.

"We finally caught him on Stapleoak," said one of the men. "He decided to fly down to us. He's had enough and so have we. Just wanted to say thanks for your help."

"I'm glad you caught him," said the priest. "I was getting worried about all of you."

"Cheers mate. Nice one."

And with that, they took one very exhausted Harris' Hawk back to his home.

* * * * * *

At the end of the Carol Service that evening, all the people crowded into the house for mince pies and coffee. After they had gone, I crept into the church and went to my usual sleeping place.

"All the fuss about the hawk," I said out loud. "When all is said and done, he was trespassing on *my* territory."

"It's as well he wasn't one of us," said Pericles, the Peregrine Falcon in the Towneley Coat of Arms. "Had he been one of us then you would have known about it."

"Why?" I asked.

"Because we Peregrine Falcons don't hang about in trees. We swoop down from a great height and with tremendous speed to catch our prey without warning." He looked directly at me. "Sometimes our prey can be – about your size."

"Oh," I said. "Thank you for letting me know."

I was rather pleased that Pericles was securely fastened to the Towneley Coat of Arms.

CHAPTER NINE

Christmas at Saint Hubert's

A few weeks later there was snow on the ground and so I decided to go into church for warmth and comfort. What a sight awaited me! Holly and ivy, all kinds of greenery and all kinds of flowers were strewn over the floor and with them all kinds of interesting smells. A lady and her teenage children were arranging the flowers on the altar and in front of the statues. Flowers, greenery and candles were displayed on all the windowsills. There was a circular arrangement of greenery and flowers in which stood candles, three purple, one rose, one white. On the sanctuary there was a tree full of coloured lights and all kinds of beautiful decorations.

Underneath the little wrought iron altar a man and his son were busily arranging straw around the figures of a cow, an ass, some sheep, and a camel. There were figures of a shepherd and a lamb and in the middle of all these they put the figures of a man and a lady who was holding a baby. At the rear of the altar they fixed a light that shone on the figures against a background of blue.

I sat there watching in wonder until I heard someone say, "There, it's Christmas Eve, the Crib is up and everything is ready for Midnight Mass."

* * * * * *

I made a mental note to go into that Crib at the earliest opportunity. It was just the place to sleep. The opportunity came as the time drew closer to midnight. The church was almost empty when I went into the Crib and then gradually people started to come in.

Some said, "Look, there's a cat in the Crib."

Others said nothing. Perhaps, because I was curled up in the straw and so still, they thought I was a new addition to the Crib figures. And in a sense I was because I have been there at Christmas ever since. I may have seemed to be asleep but I was wide awake. I heard everything that was going on – the carols, the Scriptures and prayers, even the priest's sermon.

"... The priest's sermons ... tend to jar on our high-powered and sophisticated echo-location systems."

Later that night I was disturbed by the flapping of wings.

"Hello. My name is Bartimaeus. I'm one of the bats who from time to time take up residence here."

"I'm very pleased to meet you," I said.

"I've come to wish you a happy Christmas. But I can't stay too long."

"Why not?" I asked.

"Because most of my family live in the loft of the church house, and it's a good thing to be with one's family at Christmas."

"That's a very good reason," I said.

"But there is another reason," said Bartimaeus, darkly.

He stopped flapping about and rested on the wrought iron lectern.

"It's because of the priest's sermons. We bats find that they tend to jar on our high-powered and sophisticated echo-location systems. He'll be preaching again in the morning so I really must fly. Goodnight."

And off he flew.

It's always the same with protected species. They are awfully self-important.

"Don't bother about him," said a voice from the Crib. "I'm Custard the Camel and I travel here every year with the Wise Men. It takes us forever to get here and once we've arrived we stay on for a while in spite of the sermons. It's far too much of an effort to make the return journey straight away."

It was time to have a word with my friend, Saint Hubert.

"Excuse me, Saint Hubert. It's Macavity again. I know that I'm always asking you questions, but could you tell me something about this Crib?"

"Certainly. I'm always happy to oblige. Cribs have been erected in churches at Christmas for hundreds of years. I believe that the idea first came from Saint Francis. He's over there, near to the church organ. I'm sure he'd be happy to tell you more about it."

"Hello, Miss Macavity," said Saint Francis. "I was hoping that we would have a talk. I'm told that I have quite a flair for conversing with animals and birds."

"I'm delighted to meet you, Saint Francis," I replied. "Were you the first person to make a Crib and, if so, can you tell me why you made it?"

"Well, yes, I think I was the first. My Crib was made at Greccio, Italy, in 1223. It was my way of showing how much God loves us all. You see, God gave us his only Son, Jesus, to be our

Saviour. The figures in the Crib are of the baby Jesus who was born in a stable, of his mother Mary, and of Saint Joseph her husband. Then there are figures of the cattle and the ass, in whose stable he was born, and of all the others that came to visit him – the shepherds and the Wise Men, the sheep and lambs, and ... oh yes, Custard the Camel."

"I really must tell the others about this as none of them has ever seen the Crib," I said. "Thank you so much Saint Francis and Saint Hubert and a very happy Christmas to you and to Soter the Stag."

"Happy Christmas, Macavity!" they all replied.

* * * * * *

I went into the Crib again at the morning Mass on Christmas Day. After all the people had gone I went to see Goldilocks.

"Good morning, Goldilocks, and happy Christmas. Do you know that there is a wonderful thing in the church? It's called a Crib."

"Good morning. Happy Christmas. Yes, indeed. I know all about the Crib and why it is there. In fact, it was one of my family who first told Mary that she was going to be the Mother of Jesus. And then, of course, there were other family members who gave the news of his birth to the shepherds. We were all heavily involved at the time."

It just so happened that as we were speaking, Philonous the Pheasant made an appearance.

"Hello, Macavity. I'm keeping a low profile at this time of the year, but happy Christmas, all the same."

"Happy Christmas, Philonous. Do you know about the Crib in church?"

"Stanley, Philonous and I sat before the Crib."

"I've never been in church. I tried once but people got awfully upset and shooed me away."

"Well, I noticed as I passed by that the door is open. No one is there, except the Lord of course, and I don't think he will mind if you go in."

"I'll come, too," said Stanley, who at that moment emerged from underneath the yew tree, stretched out his front paws and sat down. "Happy Christmas, everyone. I've just 'ad an early Christmas dinner. Pieces of turkey, beef, and pheasa …" He stopped short, gave Philonous a slightly guilty look, and then continued, "Aye, well best say no more, 'appen. Are we going into church then?"

And so, the three of us, Stanley, Philonous, and I, sat before the Crib.

"How good to see you," said Custard. "We are adoring the baby Jesus because today is his birthday and he is our Lord and God."

"Can we do the same?" we asked.

"Of course you can," said Custard.

"Do we 'ave to give 'im a birthday present?" enquired Stanley who, being a tomcat, can be a bit mean.

A voice came from the back of the church. It was Saint Hubert. "The best birthday present you can give him is just to say 'Thank You.'"

"Eh? Why?" asked Stanley.

"Thank him for creating us all and for loving us so very much."

"You're right," said Stanley.

And thank him we did.

That night I curled up in the Crib and settled down to sleep. It had been a full day and I was quite exhausted. I thought of all that had happened during the day and of how wonderful it was that I had celebrated Jesus' birthday with all my friends. It is so good of him to have brought me here to live in this beautiful place and to have given me such good friends. How fortunate I am to be Miss Macavity the Church Cat of Saint Hubert's, Dunsop Bridge! Before I went to sleep I purred a little prrrrayer to the One who watches over me and takes care of me, the same Lord who watches over and takes care of you.